The Kahlil Gibran Diary for 1974

My Love ....
Hoping these pages
will gather together
your thoughts and
feelings and experiences...
and put together
a garland
of
memories!

Eid Mubarak !
Peace
&
Happiness .

All my Love
Mehtab.
28.00.1973.

THE KAHLIL GIBRAN
DIARY FOR 1974

ALFRED A. KNOPF

NEW YORK

This diary contains selections from the following works by Kahlil Gibran,
published by Alfred A. Knopf, Inc.:

The Madman: Copyright 1918 by Kahlil Gibran. Copyright renewed 1946 by Comité National de
Gibran. (*Weeks of September 9, November 11, and December 2*)

The Forerunner: Copyright 1920 by Kahlil Gibran. Copyright renewed 1948 by Mary G. Gibran
and William Saxe. (*Weeks of December 31, May 13, and August 19*)

The Prophet: Copyright 1923 by Kahlil Gibran. Copyright renewed 1951 by Mary G. Gibran and
William Saxe. (*Weeks of January 14, April 1, April 22, May 20, July 22, September 2, and October 14*)

Sand and Foam: Copyright 1926 by Kahlil Gibran. Copyright renewed 1954 by Mary G. Gibran
and William Saxe. (*Weeks of February 11, April 29, June 10, July 29, October 7, and November 25*)

Jesus the Son of Man: Copyright 1928 by Kahlil Gibran. Copyright renewed 1956 by Mary G.
Gibran and William Saxe. (*Weeks of January 21, March 18, April 8, June 24, August 12,
August 26, and December 16*)

The Earth Gods: Copyright 1931 by Kahlil Gibran. Copyright renewed 1959 by Mary G. Gibran
and William Saxe. (*Weeks of January 7, March 25, July 1, July 15, September 16, and November 18*)

The Wanderer: Copyright 1932 by Alfred A. Knopf, Inc. Copyright renewed 1960 by Mary K.
Gibran. (*Weeks of February 25, June 3, August 5, and September 30*)

The Garden of the Prophet: Copyright 1933 by Alfred A. Knopf, Inc. Copyright renewed 1961 by
Mary K. Gibran (*Weeks of February 18, April 15, May 27, October 28, and December 30*)

Prose Poems: Copyright 1934 by Alfred A. Knopf, Inc. Copyright renewed 1962 by Alfred A.
Knopf, Inc. (*Weeks of January 28, June 17, November 4, and December 9*)

Spirits Rebellious: Copyright 1948 by Alfred A. Knopf, Inc. (*Week of May 6*)

Nymphs of the Valley: Copyright 1948 by Alfred A. Knopf, Inc. (*Weeks of March 11, July 8,
and September 23*)

A Tear and a Smile: Copyright 1950 by Alfred A. Knopf, Inc. (*Weeks of February 4, March 4,
October 21, and December 23*)

Frontispiece: Gibran at 25, from an oil painting by Yusef Hoyiek

This diary belongs to

_____

JANUARY

Mon	Tue	Wed	Thu	Fri	Sat	Sun
	1	2	3	4	5	6
7	8	9	10	11	12	13
14	15	16	17	18	19	20
21	22	23	24	25	26	27
28	29	30	31			

MAY

Mon	Tue	Wed	Thu	Fri	Sat	Sun
		1	2	3	4	5
6	7	8	9	10	11	12
13	14	15	16	17	18	19
20	21	22	23	24	25	26
27	28	29	30	31		

FEBRUARY

Mon	Tue	Wed	Thu	Fri	Sat	Sun
				1	2	3
4	5	6	7	8	9	10
11	12	13	14	15	16	17
18	19	20	21	22	23	24
25	26	27	28	29	30	

JUNE

Mon	Tue	Wed	Thu	Fri	Sat	Sun
					1	2
3	4	5	6	7	8	9
10	11	12	13	14	15	16
17	18	19	20	21	22	23
24	25	26	27	28	29	30

MARCH

Mon	Tue	Wed	Thu	Fri	Sat	Sun
				1	2	3
4	5	6	7	8	9	10
11	12	13	14	15	16	17
18	19	20	21	22	23	24
25	26	27	28	29	30	31

JULY

Mon	Tue	Wed	Thu	Fri	Sat	Sun
1	2	3	4	5	6	7
8	9	10	11	12	13	14
15	16	17	18	19	20	21
22	23	24	25	26	27	28
29	30	31				

APRIL

Mon	Tue	Wed	Thu	Fri	Sat	Sun
1	2	3	4	5	6	7
8	9	10	11	12	13	14
15	16	17	18	19	20	21
22	23	24	25	26	27	28
29	30					

AUGUST

Mon	Tue	Wed	Thu	Fri	Sat	Sun
			1	2	3	4
5	6	7	8	9	10	11
12	13	14	15	16	17	18
19	20	21	22	23	24	25
26	27	28	29	30	31	

SEPTEMBER

Mon	Tue	Wed	Thu	Fri	Sat	Sun
						1
2	3	4	5	6	7	8
9	10	11	12	13	14	15
16	17	18	19	20	21	22
23	24	25	26	27	28	29
30						

OCTOBER

Mon	Tue	Wed	Thu	Fri	Sat	Sun
	1	2	3	4	5	6
7	8	9	10	11	12	13
14	15	16	17	18	19	20
21	22	23	24	25	26	27
28	29	30	31			

NOVEMBER

Mon	Tue	Wed	Thu	Fri	Sat	Sun
				1	2	3
4	5	6	7	8	9	10
11	12	13	14	15	16	17
18	19	20	21	22	23	24
25	26	27	28			

DECEMBER

Mon	Tue	Wed	Thu	Fri	Sat	Sun
						1
2	3	4	5	6	7	8
9	10	11	12	13	14	15
16	17	18	19	20	21	22
23	24	25	26	27	28	29
30	31					

New Year's Day: January 1st

Kahlil Gibran's Birthday:
January 6th (1883)

Lincoln's Birthday: February 12th

St. Valentine's Day: February 14th

Washington's Birthday: February 18th

Ash Wednesday: February 27th

St. Patrick's Day: March 17th

Palm Sunday: April 7th

Passover: April 7th

Good Friday: April 12th

Easter Sunday: April 14th

Mother's Day: May 12th

Memorial Day: May 27th

Father's Day: June 16th

Independence Day: July 4th

Labor Day: September 2nd

Rosh Hashanah: September 17th

Yom Kippur: September 26th

Columbus Day: October 14th

Veterans Day: October 28th

Halloween: October 31st

Election Day: November 5th

Thanksgiving Day: November 28th

Channukah: December 9th

Christmas Day: December 25th

Numberless Are the Kings

Then rising he leaned upon his reed and said, "Go now to the great city and sit at its gate and watch all those who enter into it and those who go out. And see that you find him who, though born a king, is without kingdom; and him who though ruled in flesh rules in spirit—though neither he nor his subjects know this; and him also who but seems to rule yet is in truth slave of his own slaves."

After he had said these things he smiled on me, and there were a thousand dawns upon his lips. Then he turned and walked away into the heart of the forest.

And I returned to the city, and I sat at its gate to watch the passersby even as he had told me. And from that day to this numberless are the kings whose shadows have passed over me and few are the subjects over whom my shadow has passed.

The *week of* December 31st *to* January 6th

Monday

Tuesday

Wednesday

The week of December 31st to January 6th

Thursday

Friday

The *week of* December 31st *to* January 6th

Saturday

Sunday

The Instrument of the Gods

In man we seek a mouthpiece,
And in his life our self-fulfillment.
Whose heart shall echo our voice if the human heart is
    deafened with dust?
Who shall behold our shining if man's eye is blinded with
    night?

The week of January 7th *to* January 13th

Monday

Tuesday

Wednesday

The week of January 7th to January 13th

Thursday

Friday

The week of January 7th to January 13th

Saturday

Sunday

The week of January 14th *to* January 20th

Monday

Tuesday

Wednesday

The week of January 14th to January 20th

Thursday

Friday

The week of January 14th to January 20th

Saturday

Sunday

He Was a Good Carpenter

He was a good carpenter. The doors He fashioned were never unlocked by thieves, and the windows He made were always ready to open to the east wind and to the west.

And He made chests of cedar wood, polished and enduring, and plows and pitchforks strong and yielding to the hand.

And He carved lecterns for our synagogues. He carved them out of the golden mulberry; and on both sides of the support, where the sacred book lies, He chiseled wings outspreading; and under the support, heads of bulls and doves, and large-eyed deer.

All this He wrought in the manner of the Chaldeans and the Greeks. But there was that in His skill which was neither Chaldean nor Greek.

The week of January 21st *to* January 27th

Monday

Tuesday

Wednesday

The *week of* January 21st *to* January 27th

Thursday

Friday

The *week of* January 21st *to* January 27th

Saturday

Sunday

The Music of the Spheres

My soul counseled me and charged me to listen for voices
    that rise neither from the tongue nor the throat.
Before that day I heard but dully, and naught save clamor
    and loud cries came to my ears;
But now I have learned to listen to silence,
To hear its choirs singing the songs of ages,
Chanting the hymns of space, and disclosing the secrets
    of eternity.

The *week of* January 28th *to* February 3rd

Monday

Tuesday

Wednesday

Thursday

Friday

The week of January 28th to February 3rd

Saturday

Sunday

The City of the Past

And I observed and saw places of work sitting like great giants beneath the wings of slumber. And sanctuaries of words around which hovered souls crying out in despair—and singing in hope. I beheld temples of religion set up by faith and destroyed by doubting. And minarets of thoughts rising heavenward like hands uplifted for alms.

Streets of desires flowing like rivers between hills I saw. And storehouses of secrets guarded by silence and plundered by thieves of inquiring. Towers of progress built by courage and overthrown by fear.

Palaces of dreams that the nights adorned and awakening spoiled. Dwellings of littleness inhabited by weakness; and places of aloneness wherein rose self-denial. Meeting-places of knowledge illumined by wisdom and darkened by folly. Wineshops of love wherein lovers drank, mocked by emptiness.

Stages of life whereon Life plays her piece; to which Death comes to end his tragedy.

That, then, is the City of the Past. A city far off, yet near; seen and unseen.

Then Life walked before me and said: "Follow me, for we have tarried long." And I asked: "Whither now, Life?" She answered: "To the City of the Future." Said I: "Have pity, for the journey has surely wearied me, and my feet have trodden stones, and obstacles have drunk my strength."

"Come, for only the coward tarries, and it is folly to look back on the City of the Past."

The *week of* February 4th *to* February 10th

The *week of* February 4th *to* February 10th

Thursday

Friday

Saturday

Sunday

Talk

In truth we talk only to ourselves, but sometimes we talk loud enough that others may hear us.

The week of February 11th *to* February 17th

Monday

Tuesday

Wednesday

The week of February 11th to February 17th

Thursday

Friday

The week of February 11th *to* February 17th

Saturday

Sunday

The week of February 18th to February 24th

Monday

Tuesday

Wednesday

The week of February 18th to February 24th

Thursday

Friday

The week of February 18th to February 24th

Saturday

Sunday

The River

In the valley of Kadisha where the mighty river flows, two little streams met and spoke to one another.

One stream said, "How came you, my friend, and how was your path?"

And the other answered, "My path was most encumbered. The wheel of the mill was broken, and the master farmer who used to conduct me from my channel to his plants is dead. I struggled down oozing with the filth of those who do naught but sit and bake their laziness in the sun. But how was your path, my brother?"

And the other stream answered and said, "Mine was a different path. I came down the hills among fragrant flowers and shy willows; men and women drank of me with silvery cups, and little children paddled their rosy feet at my edges, and there was laughter all about me, and there were sweet songs. What a pity that your path was not so happy."

At that moment the river spoke with a loud voice and said, "Come in, come in, we are going to the sea. Come in, come in, speak no more. Be with me now. We are going to the sea. Come in, come in, for in me you shall forget your wanderings, sad or gay. Come in, come in. And you and I will forget all our ways when we reach the heart of our mother the sea."

The week of February 25th to March 3rd

Thursday

Friday

The week of February 25th to March 3rd

Saturday

Sunday

⚜ *Spring* ⚜

Come, my beloved, let us walk among the little hills, for the snows have melted and life is awakened from its sleep and wanders through the hills and valleys.

Come, let us follow the footsteps of spring in the far-off field;

Come and we will ascend the heights and look upon the waving greenness of the plains below.

The week of March 4th to March 10th

Monday

Tuesday

Wednesday

The week of March 4th to March 10th

Thursday

Friday

Saturday

Sunday

❖ *The Simple Life* ❖

Those of us who have spent the greater part of our existence in crowded cities know little of the life of the inhabitants of the villages and hamlets tucked away in Lebanon. We are carried along on the current of modern civilization. We have forgotten—or so we tell ourselves—the philosophy of that beautiful and simple life of purity and spiritual cleanliness. If we turned and looked we would see it smiling in the spring; drowsing with the summer sun; harvesting in the autumn; and in the winter at rest; like our mother Nature in all her moods. We are richer in material wealth than those villagers; but their spirit is a nobler spirit than ours. We sow much but reap nothing. But what they sow they also reap. We are the slaves of our appetites; they, the children of their contentment. We drink the cup of life, a liquid clouded with bitterness, despair, fear, weariness. They drink of it clear.

The *week of* March 11th *to* March 17th

Tuesday

Wednesday

The week of March 11th to March 17th

Thursday

Friday

The week of March 11th to March 17th

Saturday

Sunday

The week of March 18th to March 24th

Monday

Tuesday

Wednesday

The *week of* March 18th *to* March 24th

The *week of* March 18th *to* March 24th

✣ *Creation* ✣

When out of chaos came the earth, and we, sons of the beginning, beheld each other in the lustless light, we breathed the first hushed, tremulous sound that quickened the currents of air and sea.

Then we walked, hand in hand, upon the gray infant world, and out of the echoes of our first drowsy steps time was born, a fourth divinity, that sets his feet upon our footprints, shadowing our thoughts and desires, and seeing only with our eyes.

And unto earth came life, and unto life came the spirit, the winged melody of the universe. And we ruled life and spirit, and none save us knew the measure of the years nor the weight of years' nebulous dreams, till we, at noontide of the seventh æon, gave the sea in marriage to the sun.

And from the inner chamber of their nuptial ecstasy, we brought man, a creature who, though yielding and infirm, bears ever the marks of his parentage.

The *week of* March 25th *to* March 31st

Monday

Tuesday

Wednesday

Thursday

Friday

The week of March 25th *to* March 31st

Saturday

Sunday

⊹ *Giving* ⊹

There are those who give little of the much which they have—and they give it for recognition and their hidden desire makes their gifts unwholesome.

And there are those who have little and give it all.

These are the believers in life and the bounty of life, and their coffer is never empty.

There are those who give with joy, and that joy is their reward.

And there are those who give with pain, and that pain is their baptism.

And there are those who give and know not pain in giving, nor do they seek joy, nor give with mindfulness of virtue;

They give as in yonder valley the myrtle breathes its fragrance into space.

Through the hands of such as these God speaks, and from behind their eyes He smiles upon the earth.

Saturday

Sunday

✦ *Giving* ✦

There are those who give little of the much which they have—and they give it for recognition and their hidden desire makes their gifts unwholesome.

And there are those who have little and give it all.

These are the believers in life and the bounty of life, and their coffer is never empty.

There are those who give with joy, and that joy is their reward.

And there are those who give with pain, and that pain is their baptism.

And there are those who give and know not pain in giving, nor do they seek joy, nor give with mindfulness of virtue;

They give as in yonder valley the myrtle breathes its fragrance into space.

Through the hands of such as these God speaks, and from behind their eyes He smiles upon the earth.

The week of April 1st to April 7th

Monday

Tuesday

Wednesday

The week of April 1st *to* April 7th

Thursday

Friday

The week of April 1st *to* April 7th

✦ *Fulfillment* ✦

We ate little yet we were filled; and we drank but a drop, for we felt that the cup was like a space between this land and another land.

Then Jesus said, "Ere we leave this board let us rise and sing the joyous hymns of Galilee."

And we rose and sang together, and His voice was above our voices, and there was a ringing in every word of His words.

The *week of* April 8th *to* April 14th

Monday

Tuesday

Wednesday

The week of April 8th *to* April 14th

Thursday

Friday

The week of April 8th to April 14th

Saturday

Sunday

✦ Speak Less of God ✦

My mariners and my friends, it were wiser to speak less of
God, whom we cannot understand, and more of each other,
whom we may understand. Yet I would have you know
that we are the breath and the fragrance of God. We are
God, in leaf, in flower, and oftentimes in fruit.

The week of April 15th to April 21st

Monday

Tuesday

Wednesday

The week of April 15th to April 21st

Thursday

Friday

The week of April 15th *to* April 21st

Saturday

Sunday

The week of April 22nd *to* April 28th

Monday

Tuesday

Wednesday

The *week of* April 22nd *to* April 28th

Thursday

Friday

The week of April 22nd *to* April 28th

Saturday

Sunday

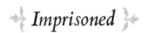

Imprisoned

We are all prisoners but some of us are in cells with windows and some without.

The week of April 29th *to* May 5th

Monday

Tuesday

Wednesday

The week of April 29th *to* May 5th

Thursday

Friday

The week of April 29th *to* May 5th

Saturday

Sunday

Eternal Justice

Plants suck up the elements of the soil; sheep feed off the plants, and the wolf preys upon the sheep. The unicorn slays the wolf, the lion hunts the unicorn, and death in its turn destroys the lion. Is there a force mightier than death to forge this chain of cruelties with an enduring justice? Is there a power that will turn these hateful things to good ends? Is there a power that will gather up all life's elements in its hand and merge them smiling in itself as the ocean gathers back to its depths all the streams in song?

The week of May 6th *to* May 12th

Monday

Tuesday

Wednesday

The week of May 6th *to* May 12th

Thursday

Friday

The week of May 6th *to* May 12th

Saturday

Sunday

The Weathercock

Said the weathercock to the wind, "How tedious and monotonous you are! Can you not blow any other way but in my face? You disturb my God-given stability."

And the wind did not answer. It only laughed in space.

The week of May 13th to May 19th

Monday

Tuesday

Wednesday

The week of May 13th *to* May 19th

Thursday

Friday

The week of May 13th *to* May 19th

Saturday

Sunday

✢ *Life Is Lived Day by Day* ✢

Your daily life is your temple and your religion.
Whenever you enter into it take with you your all.
Take the plow and the forge and the mallet and the lute,
The things you have fashioned in necessity or for delight.
For in reverie you cannot rise above your achievements
    nor fall lower than your failures.
And take with you all men:
For in adoration you cannot fly higher than their hopes
    nor humble yourself lower than their despair.

The week of May 20th to May 26th

Monday

Tuesday

Wednesday

The *week of* May 20th *to* May 26th

Thursday

Friday

The week of May 20th *to* May 26th

Saturday

Sunday

The week of May 27th *to* June 2nd

Monday

Tuesday

Wednesday

The week of May 27th *to* June 2nd

Thursday

Friday

The week of May 27th to June 2nd

Saturday

Sunday

✦ *Finding God* ✦

Two men were walking in the valley, and one man pointed with his finger toward the mountainside, and said, "See you that hermitage? There lives a man who has long divorced the world. He seeks but after God, and naught else upon this earth."

And the other man said, "He shall not find God until he leaves his hermitage, and the aloneness of his hermitage, and returns to our world, to share our joy and pain, to dance with our dancers at the wedding feast, and to weep with those who weep around the coffins of our dead."

And the other man was convinced in his heart, though in spite of his conviction he answered, "I agree with all that you say, yet I believe the hermit is a good man. And may it not well be that one good man by his absence does better than the seeming goodness of these many men?"

The week of June 3rd *to* June 9th

Monday

Tuesday

Wednesday

The week of June 3rd to June 9th

Thursday

Friday

The week of June 3rd *to* June 9th

Saturday

Sunday

The Soiled Garment

Let him who wipes his soiled hands with your garment take your garment. He may need it again; surely you would not.

The week of June 10th to June 16th

Monday

Tuesday

Wednesday

The *week of* June 10th *to* June 16th

Thursday

Friday

The week of June 10th to June 16th

Saturday

Sunday

At the Door of the Temple

I purified my lips with the sacred fire to speak of love,
But when I opened my lips I found myself speechless.
Before I knew love, I was wont to chant the songs of love,
But when I learned to know, the words in my mouth
    became naught save breath,
And the tunes within my breast fell into deep silence.

The week of June 17th to June 23rd

Monday

Tuesday

Wednesday

Thursday

Friday

The week of June 17th to June 23rd

Saturday

Sunday

⊷{ *Insight* }⊶

Methinks it was by the power of opposition and resistance
that He healed the sick, but in a manner unknown to our
philosophers. He astonished fever with His snowlike touch
and it retreated; and He surprised the hardened limbs with
His own calm and they yielded to Him and were at peace.

He knew the ebbing sap within the furrowed bark—but
how He reached the sap with His fingers I do not know.
He knew the sound steel underneath the rust—but how
He freed the sword and made it shine no man can tell.

The week of June 24th to June 30th

Monday

Tuesday

Wednesday

The week of June 24th to June 30th

Thursday

Friday

The week of June 24th *to* June 30th

Saturday

Sunday

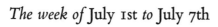

Monday

Tuesday

Wednesday

The week of July 1st *to* July 7th

Thursday

Friday

The week of July 1st to July 7th

Saturday

Sunday

There Is No Division

On the one side, power in its velvets and satins; on the other, misery in its rags and tatters. Here wealth and power personifying the religion with its songs and chants; there an enfeebled people, humble and poor, rejoicing in its secret soul in the Resurrection. Praying in silence and sighing sighs that rose from the bottom of broken hearts to float on the ether and whisper into the ears of the air. Here the leaders and headmen to whom power gave life like the life of the evergreen cypress tree. There the peasants who submit, whose existence is a ship with Death for its captain; whose rudder is broken by the waves and whose sails are torn by the winds; now rising, now sinking between the anger of the deep and the terror of the storm. Here harsh tyranny; there blind obedience. Which one is parent to the other? Is tyranny a strong tree that grows not except on low ground? Or is submission an abandoned field in which naught lives but thorns?

The week of July 8th to July 14th

Monday

Tuesday

Wednesday

The week of July 8th to July 14th

Thursday

Friday

The week of July 8th to July 14th

Saturday

Sunday

Divine Food

Aye, man is meat for gods!
And all that is man shall come upon the gods' eternal board!
The pain of childbearing and the agony of childbirth,
The blind cry of the infant that pierces the naked night,
And the anguish of the mother wrestling with the sleep
   she craves,
To pour life exhausted from her breast;
The flaming breath of youth tormented,
And the burdened sobs of passion unspent;
The dripping brows of manhood tilling the barren land,
And the regret of pale old age when life against life's will
Calls to the grave.
Behold this is man!
A creature bred on hunger and made food for hungry gods.

The week of July 15th *to* July 21st

Monday

Tuesday

Wednesday

The week of July 15th to July 21st

Thursday

Friday

The week of July 15th to July 21st

Saturday

Sunday

✥ The Purity of Love ✥

And let there be no purpose in friendship save the deepening of the spirit.

For love that seeks aught but the disclosure of its own mystery is not love but a net cast forth: and only the unprofitable is caught.

The week of July 15th *to* July 21st

Saturday

Sunday

The Purity of Love

And let there be no purpose in friendship save the deepening of the spirit.

For love that seeks aught but the disclosure of its own mystery is not love but a net cast forth: and only the unprofitable is caught.

The week of July 22nd to July 28th

Monday

Tuesday

Wednesday

The week of July 22nd to July 28th

Thursday

Friday

The week of July 22nd *to* July 28th

Saturday

Sunday

✢{ *The Madman* }✢

A madman is not less a musician than you or myself; only
the instrument on which he plays is a little out of tune.

The week of July 29th to August 4th

Monday

Tuesday

Wednesday

The week of July 29th *to* August 4th

Thursday

Friday

The week of July 29th *to* August 4th

Saturday

Sunday

❖ *The Full Moon* ❖

The full moon rose in glory upon the town, and all the
dogs of that town began to bark at the moon.

Only one dog did not bark, and he said to them in a
grave voice, "Awake not stillness from her sleep, nor bring
you the moon to the earth with your barking."

Then all the dogs ceased barking, in awful silence. But
the dog who had spoken to them continued barking for
silence, the rest of the night.

The week of August 5th to August 11th

Monday

Tuesday

Wednesday

The week of August 5th to August 11th

Thursday

Friday

The week of August 5th *to* August 11th

Saturday

Sunday

The week of August 12th to August 18th

Monday

Tuesday

Wednesday

The *week of* August 12th *to* August 18th

Thursday

Friday

The week of August 12th *to* August 18th

Saturday

Sunday

⊹⟨ *Desire For Life* ⟩⊹

And when you were a silent word upon Life's quivering lips, I too was there, another silent word. Then Life uttered us and we came down the years throbbing with memories of yesterday and with longing for tomorrow, for yesterday was death conquered and tomorrow was birth pursued.

The week of August 19th to August 25th

Monday

Tuesday

Wednesday

The week of August 19th to August 25th

Thursday

Friday

The *week of* August 19th *to* August 25th

The Little Things

Oftentimes I have seen Him bending down to touch the
blades of grass. And in my heart I have heard Him say:
"Little green things, you shall be with me in my kingdom,
even as the oaks of Besan, and the cedars of Lebanon."

He loved all things of loveliness, the shy faces of children,
and the myrrh and frankincense from the south.

He loved a pomegranate or a cup of wine given Him in
kindness; it mattered not whether it was offered by a
stranger in the inn or by a rich host.

And He loved the almond blossoms. I have seen Him
gathering them into His hands and covering His face
with the petals, as though He would embrace with His
love all the trees in the world.

The week of August 26th *to* September 1st

Monday

Tuesday

Wednesday

The week of August 26th *to* September 1st

Thursday

Friday

The week of August 26th *to* September 1st

Saturday

Sunday

Love

Like sheaves of corn he gathers you unto himself.
He threshes you to make you naked.
He sifts you to free you from your husks.
He grinds you to whiteness.
He kneads you until you are pliant;
And then he assigns you to his sacred fire, that you may
    become sacred bread for God's sacred feast.

The week of September 2nd *to* September 8th

Monday

Tuesday

Wednesday

The week of September 2nd *to* September 8th

Thursday

Friday

The week of September 2nd *to* September 8th

Saturday

Sunday

❧ *Faces* ❧

I have seen a face with a thousand countenances, and a face that was but a single countenance as if held in a mold.

I have seen a face whose sheen I could look through to the ugliness beneath, and a face whose sheen I had to lift to see how beautiful it was.

I have seen an old face much lined with nothing, and a smooth face in which all things were graven.

I know faces, because I look through the fabric my own eye weaves, and behold the reality beneath.

The week of September 9th to September 15th

Monday

Tuesday

Wednesday

The *week of* September 9th *to* September 15th

Thursday

Friday

The week of September 9th *to* September 15th

    Saturday

    Sunday

✦ True Education ✦

Youth is a beautiful dream, but its sweetness is enslaved by the dullness of books and its awakening is a harsh one.

Shall there come a day when wise men are able to unite the dreams of youth and the delights of learning as reproach brings together hearts in conflict? Shall there come a day when man's teacher is nature, and humanity is his book and life his school? Will that day be?

The week of September 16th to September 22nd

Saturday

Sunday

The week of September 16th *to* September 22nd

Thursday

Friday

The *week of* September 16th *to* September 22nd

Monday

Tuesday

Wednesday

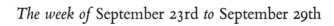

The week of September 23rd *to* September 29th

Monday

Tuesday

Wednesday

The week of September 23rd *to* September 29th

Thursday

Friday

Saturday

Sunday

The Exchange

Once upon a crossroad a poor Poet met a rich Stupid, and they conversed. And all that they said revealed but their discontent.

Then the Angel of the Road passed by, and he laid his hand upon the shoulders of the two men. And behold, a miracle: the two men had now exchanged their possessions.

And they parted. But strange to relate, the Poet looked and found naught in his hand but dry moving sand; and the Stupid closed his eyes and felt naught but moving cloud in his heart.

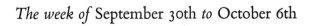

The week of September 30th to October 6th

Monday

Tuesday

Wednesday

The week of September 30th *to* October 6th

Thursday

Friday

The week of September 30th *to* October 6th

Saturday

Sunday

❖ *The Seed* ❖

A pearl is a temple built by pain around a grain of sand.
What longing built our bodies and around what grains?

The week of October 7th *to* October 13th

Monday

Tuesday

Wednesday

Thursday

Friday

The week of October 7th *to* October 13th

Saturday

Sunday

❖{ *All Men Are Equal* }❖

Oftentimes have I heard you speak of one who commits a wrong as though he were not one of you, but a stranger unto you and an intruder upon your world.

But I say that even as the holy and the righteous cannot rise beyond the highest which is in each one of you,

So the wicked and the weak cannot fall lower than the lowest which is in you also.

And as a single leaf turns not yellow but with the silent knowledge of the whole tree,

So the wrongdoer cannot do wrong without the hidden will of you all.

Like a procession you walk together towards your god-self.

You are the way and the wayfarers.

And when one of you falls down he falls for those behind him, a caution against the stumbling stone.

Aye, and he falls for those ahead of him, who though faster and surer of foot, yet removed not the stumbling stone.

The week of October 14th to October 20th

Monday

Tuesday

Wednesday

The week of October 14th *to* October 20th

The week of October 14th to October 20th

Saturday

Sunday

The *week of* October 21st *to* October 27th

Monday

Tuesday

Wednesday

Thursday

Friday

The week of October 21st to October 27th

Saturday

Sunday

❧ The Angels Are Tired of the Clever ❧

The angels are tired of the clever. And it was but yesterday that an angel said to me: "We created hell for those who glitter. What else but fire can erase a shining surface and melt a thing to its core?"

The week of October 28th to November 3rd

Monday

Tuesday

Wednesday

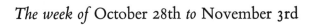

The week of October 28th to November 3rd

Thursday

Friday

The week of October 28th to November 3rd

Saturday

Sunday

Fame

I walked upon the sand at ebb tide.
And bending down, I wrote a line upon the sand.
And in that line I wrote what my mind thought
And what my soul desired.

And when the tide was high,
I returned to that very shore,
And of that which I had written I found naught.
I found only the staff-marks of one who had walked
    blindly.

The week of November 4th *to* November 10th

Monday

Tuesday

Wednesday

Thursday

Friday

The week of November 4th *to* November 10th

Saturday

Sunday

⊹ The Fox ⊹

A fox looked at his shadow at sunrise and said, "I will have a camel for lunch today." And all morning he went about looking for camels. But at noon he saw his shadow again—and he said, "A mouse will do."

The week of November 11th *to* November 17th

Monday

Tuesday

Wednesday

The week of November 11th to November 17th

Thursday

Friday

The *week of* November 11th *to* November 17th

Saturday

Sunday

The *week of* November 18th *to* November 24th

Monday

Tuesday

Wednesday

The week of November 18th *to* November 24th

Thursday

Friday

Saturday

Sunday

Perspective

It was but yesterday I thought myself a fragment quivering without rhythm in the sphere of life.

Now I know that I am the sphere, and all life in rhythmic fragments moves within me.

The *week of* November 25th to December 1st

Monday

Tuesday

Wednesday

The *week of* November 25th to December 1st

Thursday

Friday

The *week of* November 25th to December 1st

Saturday

Sunday

The Eye

Said the Eye one day, "I see beyond these valleys a mountain veiled with blue mist. Is it not beautiful?"

The Ear listened, and after listening intently awhile, said, "But where is any mountain? I do not hear it."

Then the Hand spoke and said, "I am trying in vain to feel it or touch it, and I can find no mountain."

And the Nose said, "There is no mountain, I cannot smell it."

Then the Eye turned the other way, and they all began to talk together about the Eye's strange delusion. And they said, "Something must be the matter with the Eye."

The week of December 2nd *to* December 8th

Monday

Tuesday

Wednesday

The week of December 2nd *to* December 8th

Thursday

Friday

The week of December 2nd *to* December 8th

Saturday

Sunday

❦ *The Soul* ❦

. . . And the God of Gods created the soul, fashioning it for
    beauty.

He gave unto it the gentleness of a breeze at dawn, the scent
    of flowers, the loveliness of moonlight.

He gave unto it also the cup of joy, and He said:

"You shall not drink of this cup save that you have for-
    gotten the past and renounced the future."

He gave unto it also the cup of sorrow, saying:

"Drink that you may understand the meaning of joy."

The week of December 9th *to* December 15th

Thursday

Friday

Saturday

Sunday

The week of December 16th *to* December 22nd

Monday

Tuesday

Wednesday

The week of December 16th to December 22nd

Thursday

Friday

The week of December 16th to December 22nd

Saturday

Sunday

❖ *Nativity* ❖

A mighty love it was, seated in the manger within my breast; a beautiful love swaddled in clothes of kindness. A gentle suckling lying upon the breast of the spirit, turning my grief into joy and my wretchedness to glory, and making my aloneness a pleasant thing.

A king raised high on the throne of unearthly essence, who brought back with his voice life to my dead days, and light to my weeping eyes with his touch; whose right hand snatched hope from the pit of despair.

The night has been long, my beloved, and now dawn is nigh; soon shall it be day. For the breath of the Child Jesus has filled the firmament and is merged with the air.

The week of December 23rd to December 29th

Monday

Tuesday

Wednesday

Thursday

Friday

The week of December 23rd *to* December 29th

Saturday

Sunday

Giving and Receiving

Between your right hand that gives and your left hand that receives there is a great space. Only by deeming them both giving and receiving can you bring them into spacelessness, for it is only in knowing that you have naught to give and naught to receive that you can overcome space.

The *week of* December 30th *to* January 5th

Monday

Tuesday

Wednesday

The week of December 30th to January 5th

Thursday

Friday

The week of December 30th to January 5th

Saturday

Sunday

A Note on the Type

The text of this book has been set on the Monotype in a type face named Bembo. The roman is a copy of a letter cut for the celebrated Venetian printer Aldus Manutius by Francesco Griffo, and first used in Cardinal Bembo's *De Aetna* of 1495—hence the name of the revival. Griffo's type is now generally recognized, thanks to the researches of Mr. Stanley Morison, to be the first of the old face group of types. The companion italic is an adaptation of a chancery script type designed by the Roman calligrapher and printer Lodovico degli Arrighi, called Vincentino, and used by him during the 1520's.

The book was printed by Halliday Lithograph Corp., West Hanover, Mass., and bound by The Colonial Press, Inc., Clinton, Mass. Typography and binding design by CLINT ANGLIN.